Let's Pray!

A Lesson on Prayer

If you want to be good at something
you have to practice it every day.

Like basketball, the more you 'practice' prayer, the easier it gets!

In the name of the _____
and of the _____
and of the _____ _____
Amen.

You can pray, night or day!

"I am the way, the truth, and the life.
No one can come to my Father unless they
come through me." - John 14:6

She's praying in church.　He's praying at school.　She's praying at bedtime.

Use the blank space to draw where you like to pray!

I love to pray!

"Lord, teach us to pray." - Luke 11:1

When we pray we know Jesus hears us!

"When you pray, use all that you have to bring your heart to God." - Mother Teresa

God hears your prayers.

Answer key is on the inside back cover

Find the objects hidden in the picture.

"We cannot do great things. We can only do little things with great love." Mother Teresa

God loves me and loves to hear from me.

Draw yourself praying.